Book 2

W9-CXO-183

Up

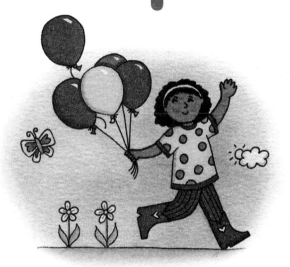

by Nancy Hechinger
Illustrated by Kathleen Kuchera

SCHOLASTIC

I see 1 ⭐.

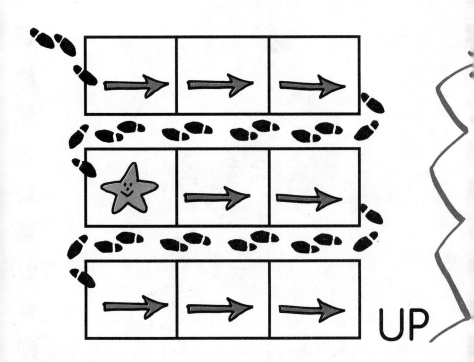

UP

2

I see 2 🍦.

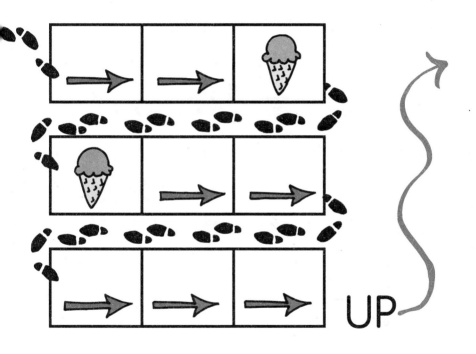

UP

3

I see 3 🦢.

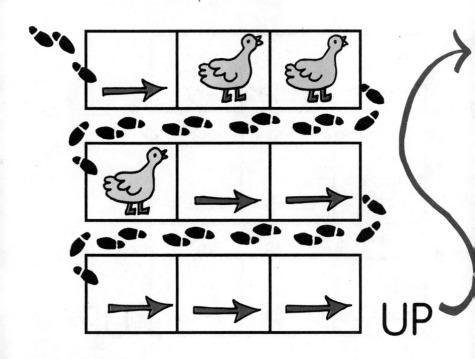

UP

4

I see 4 🌼.

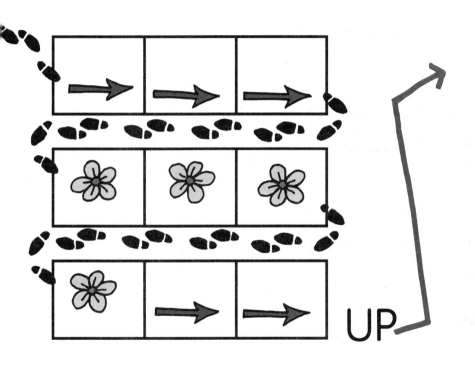

UP

5

I see 5 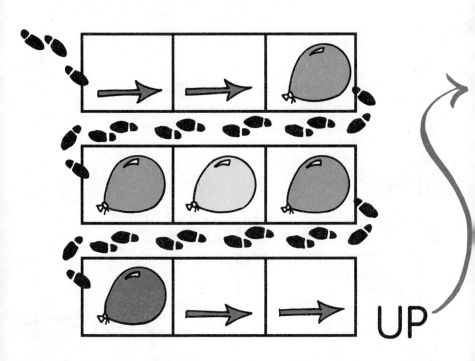.

UP

6

Up! Up! Up!

My Words

*up

*new high frequency words